Walt Disney's

Snow White
and the Seven Dwarfs

PENGUIN BOOKS

Penguin Books Ltd, Harmondsworth,
Middlesex, England
Penguin Books, 625 Madison Avenue,
New York, New York 10022, U.S.A.
Penguin Books Australia Ltd, Ringwood,
Victoria, Australia
Penguin Books Canada Ltd, 2801 John Street,
Markham, Ontario, Canada L3R 1B4
Penguin Books (N.Z.) Ltd, 182-190 Wairau Road,
Auckland 10, New Zealand

First published in this format 1980

Made and printed in Great Britain by
The Fakenham Press Ltd, Norfolk

'You should have heard the howls of warning, 'said Walt Disney, 'when we started making a full-length cartoon. It was prophesied that nobody could sit through such a thing. But there was only one way we could do it successfully, and that was to plunge ahead – go for broke . . .'

It took three years – from 1934 to 1937 – to make seven reels that added up to eighty-three pioneering minutes of pure entertainment. But the costs of 'Disney's Folly' (as some christened the project) spiralled from a budget of $150,000 to a then astronomical figure of $1,500,000. And all this at a time when America was in the midst of a crippling depression.

Disney was not prepared to compromise on any detail. Over 750 artists worked on the picture. There were 32 animators, 102 assistants, 107 in-betweeners (who fill in bits of action between the animators' drawings), 20 layout men, 25 background artists, 65 special effects animators (who draw smoke, water, clouds, etc.) and 158 professionals who specialize in inking and painting the cartoon figures on transparent celluloid sheets for reproduction by the Multiplane camera.

The Multiplane camera was used on some sequences. It was invented and developed at the Disney studios, and was designed to endow certain animated scenes with a three-dimensional quality by photographing the cartoon characters within painted backgrounds on several levels or planes. Each plane may be lit separately for effect, moved individually or jointly, closer to or farther from a camera lens, or at different speeds.

Disney was determined to extend the range of animated techniques. No one had ever drawn a girl like Snow White in animation before. Cartoons had always been flat, with more emphasis on caricature than realistic representation. Now actors were hired to pantomime the action from which hundreds of sketches were made, and from which body balance and movement could be studied.

Finding the right voice for the leading lady was also a problem. Over 150 girls were auditioned for the part. They were identified by a number, and Disney would listen to them sing and speak while he sat behind a screen. He preferred not to watch them, in case their physical appearance might influence his judgement.

Then there was the crucial business of finding precise personalities for the seven dwarfs. The Brothers Grimm's original fairy story was of no help here. So the studio played around with all sorts of names that would signal a strong personality characteristic. Gabby, Jumpy, Sniffy, Puffy, Lazy, Stubby, Shorty, Nifty, Wheezy eventually were refined to the immortal Doc, Sneezy, Happy, Grumpy, Sleepy, Bashful and Dopey. And they are still receiving fan mail at the Studios!

The picture opened at Hollywood's famous Cathay Circle on 21 December 1937. Right up to the last moment it was touch and go. With only hours to spare the Technicolor print was rushed to the theatre. But the glittering première audience, which included stars like Charlie Chaplin, Marlene

Dietrich, Charles Laughton and Judy Garland, was in no doubt that motion picture history was being made before their very eyes.

In its first three months of general release, Snow White attracted over twenty million people to the box office. It has been reissued five times – in 1944, 1952, 1958, 1967 and 1975 – and each time has surpassed its previous attendance record.

On 23 December 1939 at the Academy Awards ceremony, the tiny nine-year-old Shirley Temple presented a special trophy – one large Oscar and seven miniature replicas in stair-step arrangement alongside. It was inscribed 'To Walt Disney for *Snow White and the Seven Dwarfs,* recognized as a significant screen innovation which has charmed millions and pioneered a new great entertainment field for the motion picture cartoon.'

P. Sidey

Once upon a time, a beautiful Princess named Snow White lived in a castle
with her evil stepmother the Queen.

The Queen feared that soon Snow White's beauty would surpass her own
and each day she consulted her Magic Mirror.

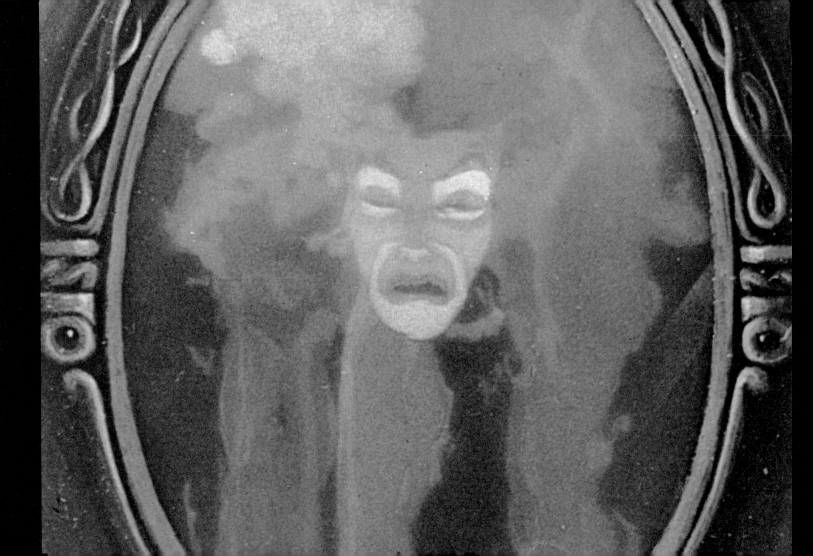

The Queen dressed Snow White in rags and forced her to work as a servant.
The birds were her only friends.

'Pigeons, do you want to know a secret?'

'Make a wish into the well   Your wish will soon come true.
That is all you have to do,   I'm wishing . . .' *Echo:* 'I'm wishing . . .'
And if you hear it echoing   'For the one I love to find me . . .' *Echo:* '. . . to find me . . .'

Unknown to Snow White a Prince approaches the castle wall

and hears Snow White singing at the well.

Prince: 'Did I frighten you?'

Frightened by the stranger Snow White runs away up the castle steps
and on to a balcony.

Prince: 'Now that I've found you   One song, only for you,
     Hear what I have to say –   One heart tenderly beating,
                                   Ever entreating,
                                   Constant and true.'

The jealous Queen watches through the curtains.

Prince: 'One song, my heart keeps singing
Of one love, only for you.'

Inside the castle the Queen angrily summons her Huntsman:
'Take her far into the forest and there, my faithful Huntsman,
you will kill her

...but he is unable to kill her and advises her to run away and hide.

Owls hoot

and branches clutch at her

until she falls exhausted to the ground

and awakes surrounded by forest animals.

They lead her through the woods

where they come to a Dwarfs' house.

The inside is very dusty and untidy so Snow White decides to clean up.

'We'll clean the house and surprise them, then maybe they'll let me stay.'

Meanwhile, down in the mine, the Dwarfs are singing as they dig for diamonds.

Oh, what adorable little beds
And look, they have their names carved on them
Doc – Happy – Sneezy – Dopey – Grumpy – Bashful and Sleepy.'

'I'm a little sleepy myself.'

'Look what's happened to our table.'

Something's up there . . . in the bedroom.'

Doc: 'Why i-i-i-it's a girl.'
Bashful: 'She's beautiful – just like an angel.'

Snow White awakes with a shock:
'Oh! Now don't tell me who you are – Let me guess. I know. . .'

Dwarfs: 'Well, who are you and what are you doing here?'
Snow White: 'Oh, how silly of me. I'm Snow White.'
Dwarfs: 'Snow White – the Princess? Well, we're honoured.'

Snow White: 'Please don't send me away – if you do the Queen will kill me.'
Grumpy: 'Huh, I'm warning you, if the Queen finds you here
she'll sweep down and wreak vengeance on us.'

Snow White: 'Oh, she'll never find me here – and if you let me stay
I'll keep house for you. I'll wash and sew and sweep and cook!

'Ah – soup – hooray!'

Snow White: 'Supper's not quite ready, you'll just have time to wash.'
Dwarfs: 'Wash!!'

The wicked Queen, having learned from the Magic Mirror
that Snow White is still alive, goes down into the dungeons.

'I'll go myself to the Dwarfs' cottage in a witch's disguise
and no one will ever suspect . . .'

'Mummy dust to make me old,
To shroud my clothes, the black of night,
To age my voice, an old hag's cackle,
To bleach my hair, a scream of fright.

Snow White and the Dwarfs pass the evening singing and dancing.
The house is full of the sound of laughter.

Everyone is enjoying themselves:

Bashful and Doc play a lively tune,

Grumpy plays the organ,

Dopey on the drums.

Happy sings: 'I like to dance and tap my feet
But they won't keep in rhythm.
You see, I washed them both today
And I can't do nothing with them.'

Snow White dances with Bashful, Sneezy and Doc.

Sneezy: 'Be careful now.'

Dwarfs: 'Now Snow White you do something.
    Tell us a story. A true story.'

'Once upon a time there was a princess,
and she fell in love . . .'

'Oh, my goodness! It's past your bedtime.'

Now that the Dwarfs know Snow White is a real princess

they insist that she sleeps in their beds
while they remain downstairs.

Back in the dungeon, the witch prepares the poisoned apple.
'Dip the apple in the brew,

'Let the sleeping death seep through,

'Now turn red to tempt Snow White,
To make her hunger for a bite.

'But wait. There may be an antidote . . . Love's first kiss –
no fear of that. The Dwarfs will think she's dead. Ha, ha.'

The next morning Snow White says goodbye to the Dwarfs as they leave for work.

Bashful: 'Be awfully careful, because if anything should happen to you, – I – ah, I – ah . . . '

Snow White: 'Don't worry. I'll see you tonight.'

Grumpy: 'Now I'm warning you.
Don't let anybody or anything into the house.'

Snow White: 'Why Grumpy, you do care for me.'

The witch approaches the cottage.
'The little men will be away . . .

'All alone, my pet?
You need apples like these for the pies you're making.'

Snow White: 'Oh, they do look delicious.'
Witch: 'But wait till you taste one.'

Witch: 'Oh, my – my – poor heart.
Take me into the house – let me rest.
A drink of water – please.'

'Quick, let us run and warn the Dwarfs.'

Doc: 'Look, everybody!'

Grumpy: 'Go on, get out of here. Go on.'
Sleepy: 'They've gone quite mad.'

Bashful: 'They aren't acting this way for nothing.'
Sleepy: 'Maybe the old Queen's got Snow White.'
Grumpy: 'The Queen will kill her. We've got to save her.'

Witch: 'Because you've been so good to poor old Granny,
I'll share a secret with you. This is no ordinary apple – it's a magic wishing apple.
One bite and all your dreams will come true.'

'I wish that my love will carry me away to his castle, where we will live happily ever after . . .'

'I'm trapped. What will I do? The meddling little fools.'

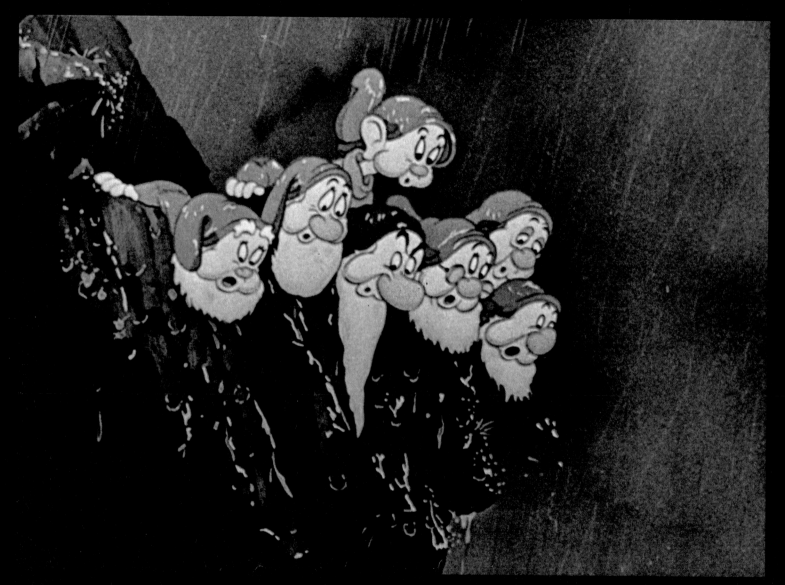

A bolt of lightning throws both witch and boulder
down into the valley below.

That night the grieving Dwarfs gather around Snow White.

She was so beautiful the Dwarfs could not bury her.
They fashioned a coffin of glass and gold and kept eternal vigil at her side.

The Prince, who had searched far and wide for Snow White, heard of the maiden
who slept in the glass coffin. He sang as he travelled over the countryside:
'One song, my heart keeps singing,
 One song, only for you.'

And they live happily ever after.